Whatever!

JIM DAVIS

ℛℛ
RAVETTE PUBLISHING

First published by Ravette Publishing 2013.
Reprinted 2014.

_____

Ravette Publishing Limited,
PO Box 876
Horsham
West Sussex RH12 9GH

www.ravettepublishing.tel

ISBN: 978-1-84161-380-2

JIM DAVIS 7-26

JIM DAVIS 7-30

WELL, IT WASN'T EASY, BUT I GOT BOTH SHOES ON THE SAME FOOT!

IS IT ANY WONDER I SLEEP 18 HOURS A DAY?

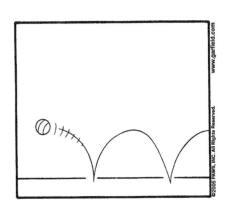